PART ONE

TIMES FABLES

HOW TO USE THIS BOOK

This book contains all the information you need to learn your 3, 4, 6, 7, 8 and 9 times tables. It may not be the traditional way to learn your times tables, but it's lots of fun, and really does work!

Don't try to figure out how the book works. To begin with, just concentrate on learning the stories. By the time you reach the end of Part 1, all will be revealed, and you'll realise that the stories that you have learnt are really just hidden multiplication problems.

Start by memorising the characters on the next page. Can you see that each character has been drawn in such a way as to look like the number it represents?

MEET THE CHARACTERS

The stories that follow each contain exactly two of the following characters:

- The robins (can you find a number 3 hidden in each bird?)

- A chair (which has the number 4 built into its frame)

- Six elves (can you see that they look like little sixes?)

- Dr Sven (she's a reindeer, but she also looks like the number 7)

- Mrs Snowman (who bears a remarkable resemblance to the number 8)

- Santa (can you see that his head is shaped like the number 9?)

Dr Sven and Mrs Snowman are best friends. They enjoy hanging out with one another and meet 5 times a week at 6 o'clock to have dinner together.

On which days do you think they meet?

Would you like to have dinner with your friends 5 times a week at 6 o'clock like Mrs Snowman and Dr Sven do?

Remember, Mrs Snowman and Dr Sven meet for dinner

5 times a week at 6 o'clock.

Mrs Snowman has a large collection of scarves, 32 in total. This means she can wear a different scarf every day of the month and still have some left over!

At the end of every month, Mrs Snowman washes and irons her 32 scarves and puts them back in her wardrobe.

Mrs Snowman uses a chair to help her put her 32 scarves away.

What do you think Mrs Snowman does with the chair? Can you think of another way Mrs Snowman might use the chair to help tidy away her 32 scarves?

32 scarves

Remember, Mrs Snowman uses a chair to put away

her collection of 32 scarves.

Dr Sven was just about to enter the hospital where she works when all of a sudden, a robin landed on her nose, making her sneeze 21 times.

That's a lot of sneezes, isn't it? Perhaps Dr Sven is allergic to robins.

Can you think of anything that might make you sneeze 21 times?

Remember, a robin landed on Dr Sven's nose and

made her sneeze 21 times.

Did you know that Santa has six elves that help him make toys for all the good boys and girls around the world?

The six elves work in a little workshop tucked away at a secret location at the North Pole.

Every year, the elves arrive at Santa's workshop exactly 54 days before Christmas, marking the start of the Christmas season.

Remember, the six elves arrive at Santa's workshop

exactly 54 days before Christmas.

People everywhere are starting to feel the Christmas spirit. This is certainly true of the red-breasted robins, one of whom lands on a chair, and starts to sing the 12 Days of Christmas rather loudly!

Do you know that song?

Perhaps you could sit on your favourite chair and sing the 12 Days of Christmas, just like the robin did!

Remember, a robin landed on a chair and started to

sing the 12 Days of Christmas.

Sadly, Mrs Snowman wasn't feeling very well.

The six elves heard she was poorly and decided to check on her.

They took her temperature and found it was a very hot 48 degrees.

Do you think the six elves were worried when they discovered Mrs Snowman had a temperature of 48 degrees? That's a very high temperature, especially for a snowman.

Remember, the six elves checked Mrs Snowman's temperature and found it was 48 degrees.

The elves were worried and decided to visit Dr Sven in her hospital to ask her for advice. They didn't want to turn up empty-handed, and so took with them 42 presents for Dr Sven's patients.

How kind of the elves to think about Dr Sven's 42 patients.

I'm sure Dr Sven's patients felt much better after seeing six elves arrive with 42 presents for them. I know I would, wouldn't you?

Remember, the six elves visited Dr Sven in her hospital and

took with them 42 presents for her sick patients.

Meanwhile, Mrs Snowman was getting hotter and hotter. What happens to snow when it gets hot? That's right, it melts! Poor Mrs Snowman!

The robins heard that Mrs Snowman was starting to melt, and flapped their wings as fast as they could to try and cool Mrs Snowman down. This worked for a while, but as soon as they stopped flapping their wings, Mrs Snowman started to melt again!

Suddenly, one of the robins had a brainwave. What if they collected 24 buckets of ice and placed the ice around Mrs Snowman? Might that stop her melting, they wondered?

Remember, to stop her melting, the robins brought Mrs Snowman

24 buckets of ice.

After her long day at work, Dr Sven returned home to find a small red sack outside her house that appeared to be full of gold coins. Next to the sack, there was a handwritten note.

The note read:

> To a very special person,
>
> Please use these gold coins to buy something nice for yourself in the new year.
>
> With much love, Santa xxx

Dr Sven tipped out the coins and counted them. There were 63 coins in total. That's an odd number, isn't it? Why do you think Santa gave Dr Sven 63 gold coins? Do you suppose it's because she lives at Number 63?

What do you think Dr Sven will buy with the 63 coins that Santa left for her? What would you buy if you were Dr Sven?

Remember, Santa left a sack outside Dr Sven's house containing 63 gold coins.

Christmas is drawing nearer, and the elves are behind schedule. There are so many presents to wrap and not enough time!

The elves decide to send a message to the robins to ask if they might be able to come and help.

The elves are very pleased when the next day, a group of 18 robins turn up to help them. Now they will be able to get all the presents wrapped in time for Christmas. Hooray!

Remember, the elves sent a message to the robins, and were delighted when a group of 18 turned up to help.

Mrs Snowman was feeling better, and decided to visit Santa.

She took Santa 7 carrots and 2 of her very best home-made mince pies – one for Santa, and another for his wife.

Who do you think the carrots might have been for?

It was very nice of Mrs Snowman to take Santa 7 carrots and 2 mince pies, wasn't it? Hopefully Santa and his wife appreciated the 7 carrots and 2 mince pies!

Remember, Mrs Snowman gave Santa

7 carrots and 2 mince pies.

Dr Sven has a very busy job, and doesn't get to sit down very often. When she does, she likes to sit in her favourite chair and dream about her holiday.

Dr Sven is very excited, as she is going to Chair-land in February. For 28 days, Dr Sven plans to do nothing but sit in a chair and relax!

It sounds boring, doesn't it? But not for Dr Sven – she can't think of anything she'd rather do than spend 28 days sitting in a comfy chair!

Remember, Dr Sven is going to Chair-land in February, where she will spend 28 days sitting in a chair!

It's almost Christmas, and the robins are no longer needed at Santa's workshop.

To mark the end of their visit, they decide to do a special fly-past for Santa and his team. Santa stands outside and watches as the robins circle around his workshop 27 times.

Do you think the robins felt dizzy after flying around Santa's workshop 27 times? What a sight it must have been for Santa watching the robins fly past 27 times! I wonder where the robins will fly to next?

Remember, Santa watched the robins circle around

his workshop 27 times.

ecember 24th – and the elves have
...ys for the good boys and girls all over
...al job left to do...

...d their final 24 hours before Christmas working as
...ey can to build a new chair for a very special person.
...hours, they work tirelessly, sawing and sanding,
...mmering and polishing to get this special chair ready.

Can you think who the elves might be making this special chair
for?

Keep reading and see if you are right!

Remember, the six elves built a special chair on

December 24th.

Christmas is over and Santa has finished delivering all his presents. It's now time for Santa to put his feet up and relax. And where better to do that than in a lovely wooden chair that he found waiting for him when he returned to the North Pole...

Santa is delighted with the chair, and sits down and falls asleep.

Poor Santa is exhausted, and sleeps for a whole 36 hours, not even waking once. Santa must have been very tired to sleep for 36 hours. But then given how far he's just travelled, is it any wonder? I expect I'd want to sleep for 36 hours after travelling around the world delivering presents too, wouldn't you?

36 hours later...

Remember, Santa slept in his new chair for 36 hours.

Believe it or not, if you can remember all the stories from the previous pages, then you now know most of your times tables!

For example, if you want to know the answer to 3 x 4, simply think of the story that includes both the robin (number 3) and the chair (number 4) and you will find the answer hidden in the story – in this case **12**, because the **ROBIN** sat on a **CHAIR** and sang the **12** days of Christmas.

Try it for yourself...

What is 8 x 6?

To get the answer, you first need to remember which character represents the number 8, and who or what represents number 6.

Next, think of the story containing these characters...

HERE'S A HINT...

The six elves took Mrs Snowman's temperature. But what was her temperature? Do you remember?

THE CORRECT ANSWER IS 48. DID YOU GET IT RIGHT?

If you didn't get the right answer, go back and re-read the stories. When you are confident that you know them all, try to answer the questions on the next page.

Here's some more for you to try:

4 x 3 =	8 x 7 =	9 x 7 =	8 x 4 =
6 x 8 =	9 x 3 =	4 x 6 =	9 x 6 =
7 x 6 =	3 x 8 =	7 x 3 =	4 x 9 =
3 x 6 =	7 x 4 =	9 x 8 =	

PART TWO

SQUARE NUMBERS

Square numbers are those multiplied by themselves.

To learn these we don't need robins, snowmen, chairs or elves.

3 times 3? Think of the rhyme,

And you'll remember that the answer is 9.

If ever you find yourself asked by the Queen,

What 4 times 4 is, please tell her 16.

High 5!
It's 25

5 times 5 is 25.

How good it is to be alive (High-Five!)

Abracadabra! Magic tricks.

6 times 6 is 36.

7 kids in 7 lines.

Add them up, it's 49.

8 times 8 is 64.

Push your (8-year-old) sister out the door.

Learning times tables is so much fun...

Just two more to go, and then we're done.

9 times 9 is 81.

Run along and eat a bun.

The easiest of all, it must be said,

10 times 10 is one hundred.

Read the square number rhymes through a few times, and

then try to answer the questions on the next page.

How many can you remember?

$3 \times 3 =$ $4 \times 4 =$ $5 \times 5 =$ $6 \times 6 =$

$7 \times 7 =$ $8 \times 8 =$ $9 \times 9 =$ $10 \times 10 =$

CONGRATULATIONS

You have completed the book, and are officially

a times tables genius!

Note to Parents

This book was written after my own child struggled to master her times tables. As a mathematician, it was frustrating watching my child struggle to recall seemingly simple multiplication facts. I thought back to my own school days, and remembered that my "favourite" multiplication fact was 7 x 8. Why? Because we lived in house number 56. A lightbulb went off in my head, and I decided to write stories and rhymes incorporating visual cues to aid recall of times tables.

The book has been split into two parts. The first section will help your child work out how to answer multiplications involving two different numbers, ranging from 3 to 9. (Note that the 2, 5 and 10 times tables are not included in this book). Encourage your child to read through the stories a few times, and then test them on the details to see how much they remember. Ask them, for example, which story involves Mrs Snowman and Dr Sven. Ask if they can remember what Mrs Snowman and Dr Sven did together in the story. You can now explain to your child that working out the answer to 7 x 8 is as simple as identifying the number hidden in the story – in this case, 56 since Dr Sven and Mrs Snowman meet 5 times a week at 6 o'clock. It might seem complicated, but it's really not!

Once your child has mastered the multiplication facts in Part 1, move on to Part 2. This section makes use of simple rhyme to help children learn the square numbers – that is, numbers multiplied by themselves, such as 3 x 3 or 4 x 4. You might even want to encourage your child to make up their own rhymes, which is an excellent way to help reinforce times tables.

Above all, have fun. As I hope this book demonstrates, learning times tables needn't be a chore. Sometimes all it takes is a different approach.

Times tables included in the book are: 3x3, 3x4, 3x6, 3x7, 3x8, 3x9, 4x4, 4x6, 4x7, 4x8, 4x9, 5x5, 6x6, 6x7, 6x8, 6x9, 7x7, 7x8, 7x9, 8x8, 8x9, 9x9, 10x10.

Jessie Wilson, Feb 2021
www.timesfables.co.uk

Published by IOM Press and printed in Great Britain.

First published in 2017. Revised edition published in 2018.

This edition published in 2021.

ISBN: 978-1-916407664